Smash

spring 2003

Published 2003

Editorial and new arrangements and engraving by Artemis Music Limited
Cover Design: Space DPS Limited

© International Music Publications Limited
Griffin House 161 Hammersmith Road London W6 8BS England

Anywhere

words and music by
Elizabeth Orton

highest chart position 55
release date 4th November 2002

did you know Orton's new album 'Daybreaker' features collaborations with Ben Watt of Everything But The Girl, the Chemical Brothers, Ryan Adams, William Orbit, Emmylou Harris and ex-Smiths guitarist Johnny Marr.

3

Beauty & The Beast

words by **Howard Ashman**   *music by* **Alan Menken**

highest chart position **10** (as double A side)

release date 4th November 2002

did you know The duo now have Benny and Bjorn writing music for them after their manager pestered the Abba songwriters over dinner after the premiere of *Chess*. Key to the deal was the fact that Bjorn's daughter was a big Steps fan.

(C): Ooh.

Tale as old as—— time, true as it can be.

Bare-ly ev-en friends, then some-bo-dy bends un-ex-pect-ed-ly.

Bring It Back

words and music by
Bernard Butler and David McAlmont

highest chart position 36
release date 28th October 2002

did you know During their seven-year hiatus, Butler released a series of solo albums for Creation while McAlmont worked on David Arnold's *Bond* theme. Now, back together, they have been dubbed the renaissance men of northern soul.

Big Yellow Taxi

words and music by
Joni Mitchell

highest chart position 16
release date 3rd February 2003

did you know This cover version of Joni Mitchell's most famous song features in the Hugh Grant comedy *Two Weeks' Notice*. However, Counting Crows fans were not impressed with the group stooping to commercial hit-making, igniting a furious debate on the web about the band's 'authenticity'.

(1.) — pa - ra - dise and put up a park - ing lot, with a
(2.) took all the trees and put 'em in a tree mu - seum, — and charged
(3.) — late last night I heard the screen door slam, — and a

1. They've paved—

Blink

words and music by
Novel Jannusi, David Clewett, Ivar Lisinski and Mick Lister

highest chart position 12
release date 21st October 2002

did you know Defending this single against accusations of man-bashing, Rose reckoned: "It's about a guy who is just flirting around and being naughty like that. I get annoyed by it and sing about it. I think a lot of girls will be able to relate to that."

can't for-give in-fi-de-li-ty, I thought we had in-fi-ni-ty. Oh,

oh, oh, oh, oh, ho, ho, this time I'm gon-na let you

sink. As soon as I

blink, you're play-ing a-round. It's mak-ing me

Can You Dig It?

words and music by
Martin Coogan

highest chart position 19
release date 3rd March 2003
did you know The Manchester band's only hit, originally released in 1991, was revived when it was used in a mobile phone advert. Since the collapse of the band, guitarist Martin Murray had taken bit-part acting roles, including one in the TV soap *Families*.

Can_____ you un-der-stand it now?_____

I'll get it through some-how._____

33

Some - one turned_ their light____ on.___
But some - one turned_ our light_

Come Into My World

highest chart position 8
release date 11th November 2002

words and music by
Cathy Dennis and Robert Davis

did you know It seems that Kylie is finally being taken seriously by the pop industry, having obliterated Whitney Houston and Prince to move from 40 to 25 in the ranks of all-time weeks spent in the charts, as verified by the *Guinness British Hit Singles* book.

Come, come, come in-to my world, won't you lift me up, up, high up - on your love? 1. Take these

42

Dirrty

highest chart position 1
release date 11th November 2002

did you know At the age of 10, Christina sang the national anthem before a Pittsburgh Steelers game. This led to a spot on the *New Mickey Mouse Club*, alongside soon-to-be rival Britney Spears.

words and music by

Dana Stinson, Christina Aguilera, Balewa Muhammad, Jasper Cameron and Reggie Noble

(Spoken:) Dirrty, filthy, nasty. Too dirrty to clean my act up.
If you ain't dirrty, you ain't here to party.

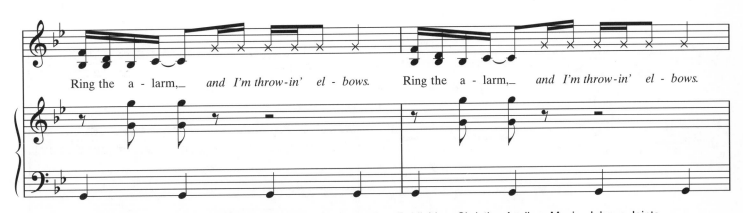

Gm7

Sweat - in' till my clothes come off. It's ex - plo - sive, speak - ers are thump - in'.

Still jump - in', six___ in the morn - in' Ta - ble danc - in', glass - es are crash - in'.

No ques - tion, time___ for some ac - tion. Tem - p'ra - ture's up, (can you feel it?)

'bout to___ e - rupt. Gon - na get my girls. Get your boys, gon - na

Chorus:

make some noise._____ Gon-na get row - dy. Gon-na get a lit - tle un -

ru - ly. Get it fired up in a hur - ry. Wan-na get dirrt - y.

It's a-bout time that I came to start the par - ty. Sweat drip-pin' o - ver my

bod - y. Danc-in' get-tin' just a lit - tle naugh - ty. Wan-na get dirrt - y.

1. It's a-bout time for my ar - riv - al.

2. It's a-bout time for my ar - riv - al. Here it

Bridge:
N.C.

comes, it's the one you been wait-in' on.___ Get up, here we go, yo, that's what's up.___ Giv-in'

just what you want to the max - i - mum.___ Uh - oh, (Uh - oh.) here we go. (Here we go.) What we

do when the mu - sic starts to drop,___ that's___ when we take it to the park - ing lot.___ And I

Verse 2:
Ah, heat is up, so ladies, fellas, drop your cups.
Body's hot from front to back.
Move your ass, I like that.
Tight hip-huggers, low, fo' sho'.
Shake a little somethin' on the floor.
I need that to get me off.
Sweatin' till my clothes come off.
Let's get up and cause a commotion.
We still goin', eight in the mornin'.
There's no stoppin', we keep it poppin'.
Hard rockin', everyone's talkin'.
Give all you got, just hit the spot.
Gonna get my girls, get your boys.
Gonna make some noise.
(To Chorus:)

Die Another Day

words and music by
Madonna Ciccone and Mirwais Ahmadzaï

highest chart position 3
release date 28th October 2002
did you know In the *Hollywood Reporter* 2002 list of the 100 most powerful women in Hollywood, Madonna had attained an impressive 60th place, making her the third highest 'celebrity' entrant behind Oprah Winfrey and Julia Roberts.

Fast ♩ = 130

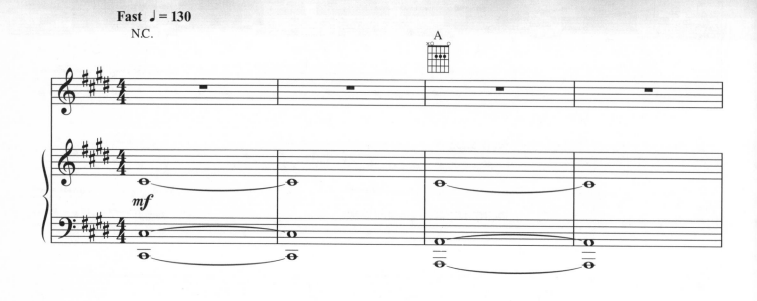

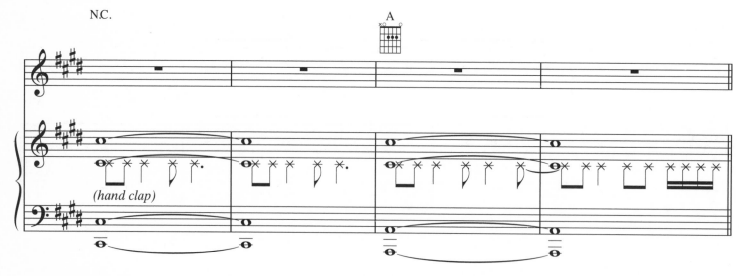

Verses 1 & 3:

1. I'm gon-na wake up, yes and no. I'm gon-na kiss some part
3. I'm gon-na a-void the cli-ché. I'm gon-na sus-pend my sen-

54

Repeat ad lib. and fade

Family Portrait

words and music by
Alecia Moore and Scott Storch

highest chart position 11
release date 9th December 2002

did you know This song's tough lyric and guitar-driven backing were utilised against record company advice, the label having tried to market Pink as a youth-friendly R&B diva. However, this fourth hit single seems to have justified the decision.

The Game Of Love

highest chart position 16
release date 11th November 2002
did you know Of working with Branch, Carlos Santana told VH1:
"Her spirit is glorious. She's not childish, even though she's very young. When you hear the song, you can hear the belief.".

words and music by
Gregg Alexander and Rick Nowels

Feel

words and music by
Robert Williams and Guy Chambers

highest chart position 4
release date 2nd December 2002

did you know As the first single to be taken from 'Escapology', this track had to prove that EMI investing £80 million in Williams wasn't the biggest gamble in the history of the music business.

Good Times Gonna Come

highest chart position 71
release date 2nd December 2002
did you know Considered by some to be "the new Moby", singer Matt Hales wrote and produced this follow-up single to 'Strange And Beautiful', which was a Top Ten hit on the back of an advert for the venerable Volkswagen Beetle.

words and music by
Matthew Hales

Help Me

words and music by

Matthew Gerrard and Michelle Vice-Maslin

highest chart position 17
release date 7th October 2002
did you know This is the first solo single from the 'cute blonde one' from Backstreet Boys. However, Carter insists that this is merely a 'side project' between BSBs recordings.

I Love Rock 'n' Roll

highest chart position 13
release date 4th November 2002
did you know A cover of Joan Jett's 1982 standard, this signals a change of direction for Britney as she attempts to bounce back from the end of her celebrity relationship with Justin Timberlake and her under-achieving road movie *Crossroads*.

words and music by
Alan Merrill and Jake Hooker

I'm Right Here

words and music by

Christian Karlsson, Henrik Jonback, Pontus Winnberg and Kandi Burruss

highest chart position 5
release date 14th October 2002

did you know Mumba has proved a big hit in America, where fans have latched on to her 'Irish' heritage – her mother comes from Ireland. Her good looks have resulted not only in modelling work, but also a film role in Spielberg's adaptation of *The Time Machine*.

1. Back in the

(1.) day   I did not know   what to look   for   in my new beau   so I would just
(2.) style,   beau - ti - ful smile,   wears that co - logne that   drives wo - men wild.   Takes more than just

Like I Love You

words and music by
Chad Hugo, Pharrell Williams and Justin Timberlake

highest chart position 2
release date 21st October 2002

did you know The velocity of Timberlake's rise can be measured by the fact that, for his multi-platinum album 'Justified', he hired hip hop star P. Diddy to re-mix one of the tracks – only to reject the finished offering, much to Diddy's disgust, as not good enough.

Ain't no - bod - y love you like I love you.

You're a good girl, and that's what makes me trust you.

Late at night I talk to you.

You will know the dif - f'rence when...

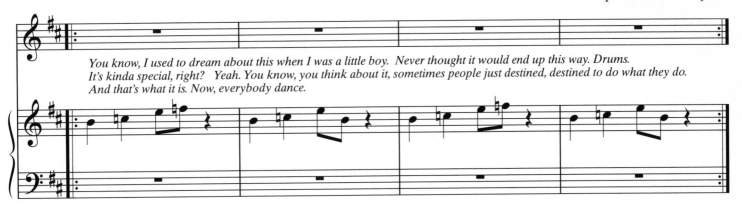

Verse 2:
Some people are so phony,
Nosy, 'cause they're lonely.
Aren't you sick of the same thing?
They say, so-and-so is dating,
Love you or they're hating,
When it doesn't matter anyway,
'Cause we're here tonight.
(To Pre-chorus:)

Rap:
Ma', whatcha wanna do?
I'm in front of you.
Grab a friend, see
I can have fun with two
Or me and you, put on a stage show.
In the mall, kids ask how the chain glow.
Point to her, say, wow, it's the same glow.
Point to me, I say, yeah, it's the same dough.
We're the same type, you're my a-alike.
You have me sleeping in the same bed every night.
Go ride with me, you're deserving the best.
Take a few shots, let it burn in your chest.
We could ride 'round pumpin' N.E.R.D. in the deck.
Funny how a few words turned into sex.
Play number 3, joint called "Brain." (I just love your brain.)
Ma' took her hand, made me swerve in the lane.
The name Malicious and I burn every track.
Clipse and J. Timberlake, now how heavy is that?
(To Bridge:)

In This World

words and music by
Moby

highest chart position 35
release date 4th November 2002
did you know He was nicknamed Moby at birth due to having
Herman Melville – the author of *Moby Dick* – as an ancestor. He grew
up in the company of three rescued pet lab rats, a cat, and a dog
named Jamie.

Last Goodbye

words and music by

**Mikkel Eriksen, Espen Lind, Amund Bjorklund,
Hallgeir Rustan, Tor Erik Hermansen
and Danny Poku**

highest chart position 2
release date 25th November 2002

did you know The band recently launched their own clothing range, named AK, at British Home Stores. It's designed to be a 'wicked' collection for six- to 13-year olds. They were given input into the designs, all of which they gave their 'paw' of approval.

1. Ain't no head-lights on the road to-night,—
2. Is it clou-dy where you are to-night?—

— ev-'ry-bo-dy is sleep-ing tight.—
Are the ne-on lights shin-ing bright?—

Ain't no-bo-dy gon-na find us here,—
Are you look-ing for a place to stay—

— we'll dis- -ap- pear.—
to get a - way?—

There's a danc-er in the arms of love—
And the days are hor-ses down the hill,—

Maybe

words and music by
David Siegel, Steve Morales, Enrique Iglesias, Kara Dio Guardi and Aaron Fishbein

highest chart position 12
release date 25th November 2002

did you know Julio's son was already a smash hit with Spanish audiences when he crossed over to the English speaking world with 1999's 'Enrique' album, which sold seven million copies. Just like his father, Enrique credits his success to the fervour of his fans.

Original key: F# major. This edition has been transposed down one half-step to be more playable.

The Opera Song
(Brave New World)

words and music by
Darren Tate, Rohan Heath and Danny Kirsch

highest chart position **3**
release date **20th January 2003**

did you know **A most unusual collaboration, combining a DJ familiar to modern Balearic dance music aficionados with former child prodigy Charlotte Church, the *Daily Mail's* idea of the perfect English chanteuse.**

Put Him Out

highest chart position 19
release date 2nd December 2002
did you know Ms Dynamite's first hit was a white label underground hit before charting, evidence that this star of the awards circuit is the authentic article – an apprentice-served garage/R&B talent with a belief in female empowerment.

words and music by
Niomi Daley, Christian Karlsson, Henrik Jonback and Pontus Winnberg

(1.) tell it like this, girl-friend he don't love you, nev-er have I seen him kiss or hug you.
2. He don't ev-en know how to be ho-nest, all he know how to do is false pro-mise.

1. Now I'm a

2.

Fm   C   Fm   C

(Oh, girl you got   to put— him out.—)   Change them locks and all   that.—

Fm   C   Fm   Eb   Ab   C

(Oh, girl you got   to put— him out.—)   And this   time— don't take him back.—

Fm   C   Fm   C

Fm   Db

Your lit-tle girl needs a dad-dy I a-gree but the fool is far——from that.——   An-y boy can
He nev-er eats with her   or takes her out,   that shit's called— ne-glect you hear. Sure,   she con-

Pussycat

words and music by

Hal David, Burt Bacharach, Wyclef Jean and Jerry Duplessis

highest chart position did not chart
release date 25th November 2002

did you know Aside from his track record as a musician, Wyclef is becoming a regular face on British TV due to his endorsements of the Virgin mobile phone network, in a series of adverts depicting the perils of breaking a contract.

Lyrics:
Pus - sy - cat, Pus - sy - cat, I love you, yes
I_____ do:_____ you and your *(fx)*

Shape Of You

words and music by
Beverley Knight and Craig Wiseman

highest chart position this album version was released as the B-side to the Wyclef Jean re-mix of 'Reshaped'.
release date 3rd March 2003
did you know Knight's progress in the charts was acknowledged in February 2003 with two Brit Award nominations, one for Best British Female Solo Artist and the other for Best UK Urban Act, though in the end she was pipped for both by Ms. Dynamite.

Ah, _____ ooh. _____ Ah, _____ oh.

1. This wo-man's eyes ain't got no co-lour, _____ when I _____
2. I step in-to un-chart-ed wa-ter, _____ and I'm a-fraid

think a-bout life with-out _____ you. _____ And ev-en if _____
of what I've _____ done. _____ See, I can't head

Sk8er Boi

words and music by
Lauren Christy, David Alspach, Graham Edwards and Avril Lavigne

highest chart position 8
release date 16th December 2002

did you know The middle of three children, Lavigne 'always wanted to be the centre of attention'. She hails from Napenee, Ontario, whose population of 5,000 was never going to hold her. As she says, 'I always knew this was what I had to do'.

Sorry Seems To Be The Hardest Word

words by **Bernie Taupin** *music by* **Elton John**

highest chart position 1
release date 9th December 2002
did you know This collaboration between the well-groomed heart-throbs and pop's Queen Mother was heavily backed to upset the *PopStars: The Rivals* Christmas Number One applecart. Sadly, it didn't

Stronger

highest chart position 7
release date 11th November 2002
did you know Keisha, Mutya and Heidi, the latter the controversial replacement of Siobhan, recently revealed their commitment to the Childline charity by playing with other top stars at a benefit at the Point Theatre.

words and music by

**Jony Rockstar, Marius De Vries, Felix Howard,
Mutya Buena, Keisha Buchanan and Heidi Range**

1. I'll make it through the rai - ny days,___ I'll be the one -
2. Some-times I feel so down__ and out,___ like e - mo-

___ who stands__ here long - er than__ the rest.___ When my land-
- tion that's__ been cap - tured in__ a maze.___ I had my

Sound Of The Underground

words and music by

Brian Higgins, Niara Scarlett and Miranda Cooper

highest chart position 1
release date 16th December 2002
did you know The winners of *Pop Stars: The Rivals*, the girly contingent Girls Aloud had to beat off male rivals One True Voice, plus the eerily amusing Cheeky Girls, for the UK's coveted Christmas Number One slot.

1. Dis - co danc - ing with the lights down low.
2. Chain re - ac - tion run - ning through my veins.

Beats are pump - ing on my ste - re - o.
Pumps still rac - ing up in - to my brain.

Then you see me ov - er - flow, where the girls get down with the sound on the ra - di - o.

Out to the 'lec - tric night, where the bass line jumps to the back - street light. The

To Coda ⊕

beat goes a-round and round, it's the sound of the un - der, sound of the un - der -

1.

Synth. N.C.

- ground.

Year 3000

highest chart position 2
release date 13th January 2003
did you know Not only was this single promoted with the usual array of limited edition CD formats and a futuristic video, but hardcore fans could also play a game which addressed a similar theme – including time travelling in the boys' own 'Busted' car.

words and music by

Steve Robson, James Bourne, Matthew Jay, Charlie Fletcher and Matthew Simpson

1. One day when I came home at lunch-time,____ I heard a fun-ny noise.
(2.) took me to the fu-ture in the flux thing,____ and I saw ev-'ry-thing:

Went out to the back-yard to find____ out____ if it was one of those rowdy boys.
boy bands and an-other one and an-oth-er one____ and an-oth-er one.

You Were Right

words and music by
Damon Gough

highest chart position 9
release date 14th October 2002

did you know Purchasers of Badly Drawn Boy's 'Have You Fed The Fish' album were invited to literally 'find' the fish. Five golden fish were released worldwide, with just one in Britain. Whoever solved the clues as to their whereabouts was invited to write a song that the band would subsequently record.

(1.) you_____ were right to bide___ your time___ and not___ buy in re-
(2.) I_____ was rush-ing round___ in cir-cles for___ a rea-

all woman

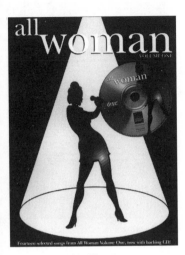

ALL WOMAN
VOLUME 1 PVG/CD 7077A

All Woman - Cabaret - Can't Stay Away
From You - Eternal Flame - Ev'ry Time We
Say Goodbye - Get Here - I Am What I Am
I Only Want To Be With You - Miss You
Like Crazy - Nobody Does It Better
The Rose - Summertime - Superwoman
What's Love Got To Do With It

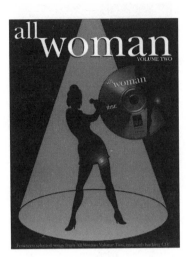

ALL WOMAN
VOLUME 2 PVG/CD 7268A

Anytime You Need A Friend
Don't It Make My Brown Eyes Blue
Flashdance....What A Feeling - I'll Stand
By You - Killing Me Softly With His Song
One Moment In Time - Pearl's A Singer
(They Long To Be) Close To You - Think
True Blue - Walk On By - The Wind
Beneath My Wings - You Don't Have To
Say You Love Me - 1-2-3

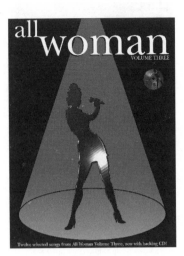

ALL WOMAN
VOLUME 3 PVG/CD 9187A

Almaz - Big Spender - Crazy For You
Fame - From A Distance - My Baby Just
Cares For Me - My Funny Valentine
The Power Of Love - Promise Me
Respect - Take My Breath Away
Total Eclipse Of The Heart

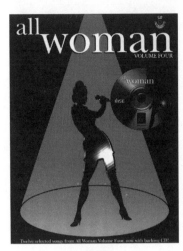

ALL WOMAN
VOLUME 4 PVG/CD 9255A

Baby Love - Diamonds Are Forever -
Evergreen - For Your Eyes Only - I Will
Survive - If I Could Turn Back Time - I'll
Be There - Rainy Night In Georgia - Send
In The Clowns - Smooth Operator - Sweet
Love - Touch Me In The Morning

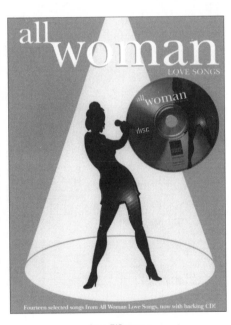

ALL WOMAN
LOVE SONGS PVG/CD 7502A

All At Once – Anything For You –
Because You Love Me – Crazy For You –
Didn't We Almost Have It All – The
Greatest Love Of All – Here We Are –
Hero – How Do I Live – I'll Never Love
This Way Again – Saving All My Love For
You – Think Twice – The Wind Beneath
My Wings – Without You

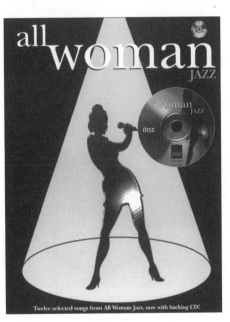

ALL WOMAN
JAZZ PVG/CD 9500A

Bewitched – Dream A Little Dream Of Me
A Foggy Day – The Girl From Ipanema
I'm In The Mood For Love – In The
Mood – It Don't Mean A Thing (If It Ain't
Got That Swing) – Misty
Nice Work If You Can Get It – On Green
Dolphin Street – 'Round Midnight
Where Or When

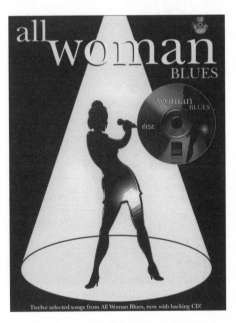

ALL WOMAN
BLUES PVG/CD 9550A

The Birth Of The Blues - Come Rain Or
Come Shine - Embraceable You -
Georgia On My Mind - Knock On Wood
Mood Indigo - Night And Day - Rescue Me
Someone To Watch Over Me
Stormy Weather
Take Another Little Piece Of My Heart -
What Is This Thing Called Love

Available from all good music shops

AW 2

YOU'RE THE VOICE

Maria Callas

8861A PV/CD

Casta Diva from Norma - Vissi D'arte from Tosca - Un Bel Di Vedremo from Madam Butterfly - Addio, Del Passato from La Traviata - J'ai Perdu Mon Eurydice from Orphee Et Eurydice - Les Tringles Des Sistres Tintaient from Carmen - Porgi Amor from Le Nozze Di Figaro - Ave Maria from Otello

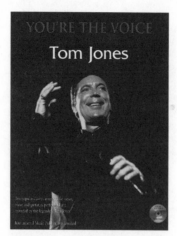

Tom Jones

8860A PVG/CD

Delilah - Green Green Grass Of Home - Help Yourself - I'll Never Fall In Love Again - It's Not Unusual - Mama Told Me Not To Come - Sexbomb Thunderball - What's New Pussycat - You Can Leave Your Hat On

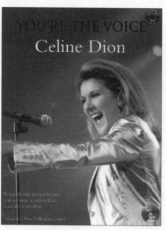

Celine Dion

9297A PVG/CD

Beauty And The Beast - Because You Loved Me - Falling Into You - The First Time Ever I Saw Your Face - It's All Coming Back To Me Now - Misled - My Heart Will Go On - The Power Of Love - Think Twice - When I Fall In Love

ARETHA FRANKLIN

9349A PVG/CD

Chain Of Fools - A Deeper Love Do Right Woman, Do Right Man - I Knew You Were Waiting (For Me) - I Never Loved A Man (The Way I Loved You) I Say A Little Prayer - Respect - Think Who's Zooming Who - (You Make Me Feel Like) A Natural Woman

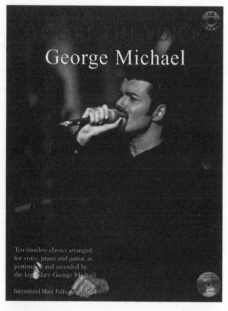

George Michael

9007A PVG/CD

Careless Whisper - A Different Corner Faith - Father Figure - Freedom '90 I'm Your Man - I Knew You Were Waiting (For Me) - Jesus To A Child Older - Outside

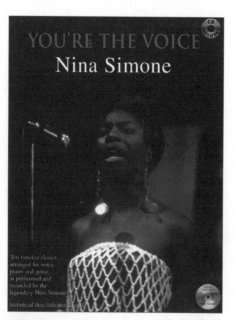

Nina Simone

9606A PVG/CD

Don't Let Me Be Misunderstood - Feeling Good - I Loves You Porgy - I Put A Spell On You - Love Me Or Leave Me - Mood Indigo - My Baby Just Cares For Me Ne Me Quitte Pas (If You Go Away) - Nobody Knows You When You're Down And Out - Take Me To The Water

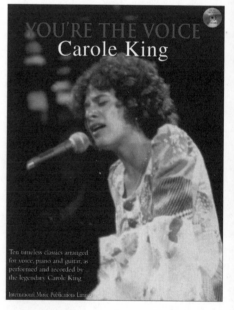

Carole King

9700A PVG/CD

Beautiful - Crying In The Rain - I Feel The Earth Move - It's Too Late - (You Make Me Feel Like) A Natural Woman So Far Away - Way Over Yonder – Where You Lead - Will You Love Me Tomorrow You've Got A Friend

The outstanding vocal series from IMP

CD contains full backings for each song, professionally arranged to recreate the sounds of the original recording